Essential Film Songs

THE ULTIMATE MO

 TAKE 2

C000160549

WISE PUBLICATIONS
London / New York / Paris / Sydney / Copenhagen / Madrid / Tokyo

YOUR GUARANTEE OF QUALITY:
As publishers, we strive to produce every book to the highest commercial standards. This book has been carefully designed to minimise awkward page turns and to make playing from it a real pleasure. Particular care has been given to specifying acid-free, neutral-sized paper made from pulps which have not been elemental chlorine bleached. This pulp is from farmed sustainable forests and was produced with special regard for the environment. Throughout, the printing and binding have been planned to ensure a sturdy, attractive publication which should give years of enjoyment. If your copy fails to meet our high standards, please inform us and we will gladly replace it.

WWW.MUSICSALES.COM

ESSENTIAL FILM SONGS: TAKE 2 PUBLISHED BY: WISE PUBLICATIONS 8/9 FRITH STREET, LONDON W1D 3JB, ENGLAND

EXCLUSIVE DISTRIBUTORS: MUSIC SALES LIMITED DISTRIBUTION CENTRE, NEWMARKET ROAD, BURY ST. EDMUNDS, SUFFOLK IP33 3YB, ENGLAND

MUSIC SALES PTY LIMITED 120 ROTHSCHILD AVENUE, ROSEBERY, NSW 2018, AUSTRALIA

ORDER NO: AM980782 • ISBN: 1-84449-648-1 • THIS BOOK © COPYRIGHT 2004 BY WISE PUBLICATIONS

UNAUTHORISED REPRODUCTION OF ANY PART OF THIS PUBLICATION BY ANY MEANS INCLUDING PHOTOCOPYING IS AN INFRINGEMENT OF COPYRIGHT

COMPILED BY NICK CRISPIN • MUSIC ARRANGED BY DEREK JONES & PAUL HONEY
MUSIC PROCESSED BY PAUL EWERS MUSIC DESIGN • COVER DESIGN BY FRESH LEMON

BANG BANG (MY BABY SHOT ME DOWN)

Words & Music by Sonny Bono

BEYOND THE SEA

Original Words & Music by Charles Trenet
English Words by Jack Lawrence

my lov - er stands on___ gold - en sands
if I could fly like___ birds on high

and watch - es the ships that go sail - - - ing.___
then straight to her arms I'll go

___ 2. Some - sail - - ing.___ It's

far be - yond the stars,___ it's

7

near   be - yond the moon.

I

*

know_____ be - yond a doubt,_____   my heart__

___   will   lead   me   there___   soon._____   We'll

meet   be - yond   the   shore,_____   we'll

8

DON'T PANIC

Words & Music by Chris Martin, Guy Berryman, Jon Buckland & Will Champion

Oh, all— that I know, there's no-thing here to run from,— cos

yeah, ev - 'ry-bo-dy here's got some-bo-dy to lean on.—

13

DON'T GIVE UP ON US

Words & Music by Tony Macaulay

15

stars. We can't change_ ours. Don't give

up on us ba - by, we're still_ worth_ one more

try. I know we've put a last one_ by,_

just for a rain - y eve - ning when may - be stars are

18

EDGE OF SEVENTEEN

Words & Music by Stevie Nicks

♩ = 108 poco accel.

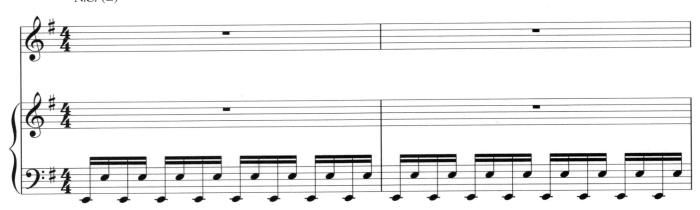

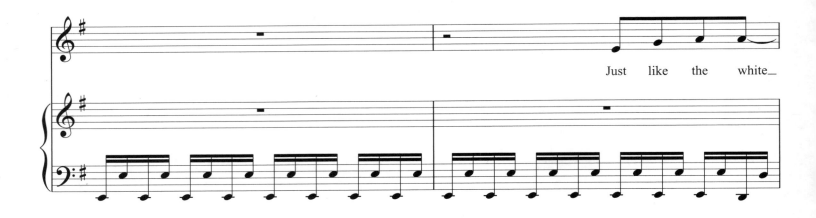

Just like the white_

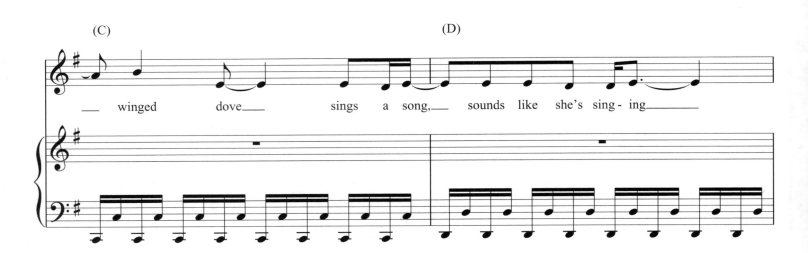

_ winged dove_ sings a song,_ sounds like she's sing-ing_

(E)

that is my own,___ I be- gin___ a - gain.___ I

(C)   (C)

said to my___ friend___ "Ba - by,_____ no - thing else___ mat -

(E)

- ters."

He was no___ more_____ than a ba -

C

D

23

28

no - one left stand - ing in the hall,___

yeah, yeah,___ in a flood___ of tears___ that

no - one real - ly ev - er heard fall at all.___

Well, I went search - ing for an ans - wer up the stairs_

34

37

EVERYBODY'S GOTTA LEARN SOMETIME

Words & Music by James Warren

Change your heart   look a-round you._

Change your heart   it will a-stound you._   And I

GHOST TOWN

Words & Music by Jerry Dammers

1. This town (town—) is 'com-in' like a
(Verse 2 see block lyric)

ghost town. All the clubs— are be-ing closed down.—

This place (town—) is 'com-in' like a ghost town.

Bands won't play no more. Too much fight-in' on the dance floor.

D.%. al Coda

⊕ Coda

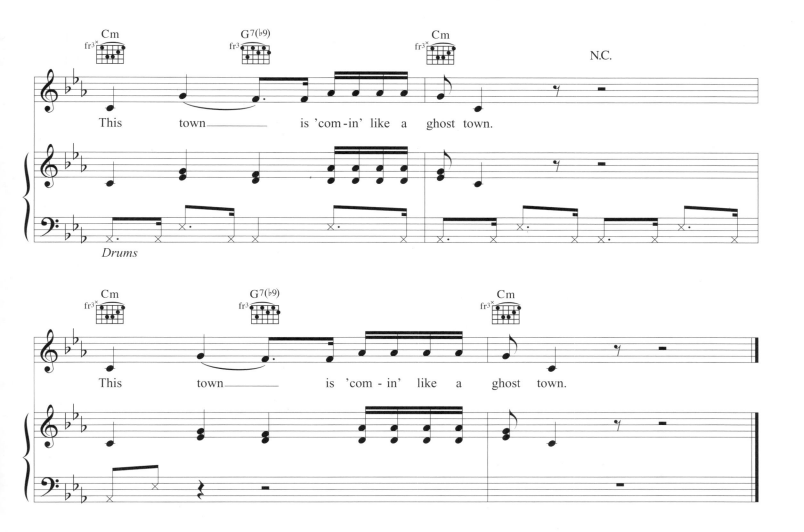

Verse 2:
This town is 'comin' like a ghost town
Why must the youth fight against themself
Government's leavin' the youths on the shelf
This place is 'comin' like a ghost town
No job to be found in this country
Can't go on no more
The people gettin' angry.

La la la la *etc.*

GOODNIGHT MOON

Words & Music by Ambrosia Parsley & Duke McVinnie

2.There's a shark in the ___

Guitar solo

3.Well you're up so high how can you save ___ me when the dark comes here to-night, you take ___ me up my front

HOLD ON

Words & Music by Nic Cester

1. You tried so hard to be___ some-one___ that you for-got___ who you___ are.___

57

THE HANDS THAT BUILT AMERICA

Words & Music by U2

of____ reach? *Vocal ad lib.*

I FOUGHT THE LAW

Words & Music by Sonny Curtis

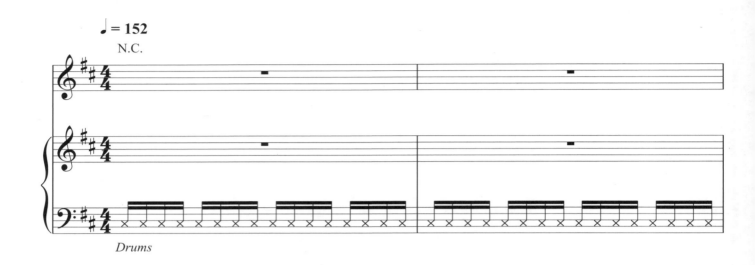

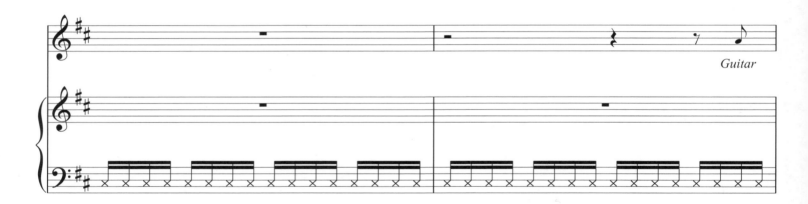

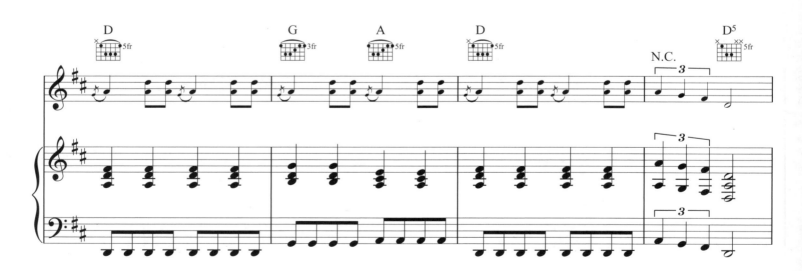

67

I'M YOUR MAN

Words & Music by Leonard Cohen

70

No chord

man.__ If you want a box - er, I will

step in - to the ring for you.__ And if you want a

doc - tor, I'll ex - am - ine ev - 'ry inch of you.__

No chord

If you want a driv - er, climb in - side.__ Or if you want to

71

take me _____ for a ride, ___ You know you can. ___

I'm your man. Ah, the

moon's too bright, ___ the chain's too tight, ___ the beast won't go to sleep. ___

— I've been run-ning through these prom-is-es to you that I

made and I could not keep.__ Ah, but a man nev-er got a

wom-an back,__ not by beg-ging on his knees.__ Or I'd

crawl to you, ba-by, and I'd fall at your feet,___ and I'd

howl at your beau-ty like a dog in heat. And I'd

claw at your heart,__ and I'd tear at your sheet. I'd say, please,__

please,__ I'm your man.__

And if you've got to sleep for a mo - ment

on the road,__ I will steer for you.__ And if you want to

work the street a-lone,_ I'll dis - ap - pear for you.

If you want a fa - ther____ for your child,_ or on-ly want to

walk with me a - while a - cross the sand,_

I'm your man._

INTO THE WEST

Words & Music by Annie Lennox, Howard Shore & Fran Walsh

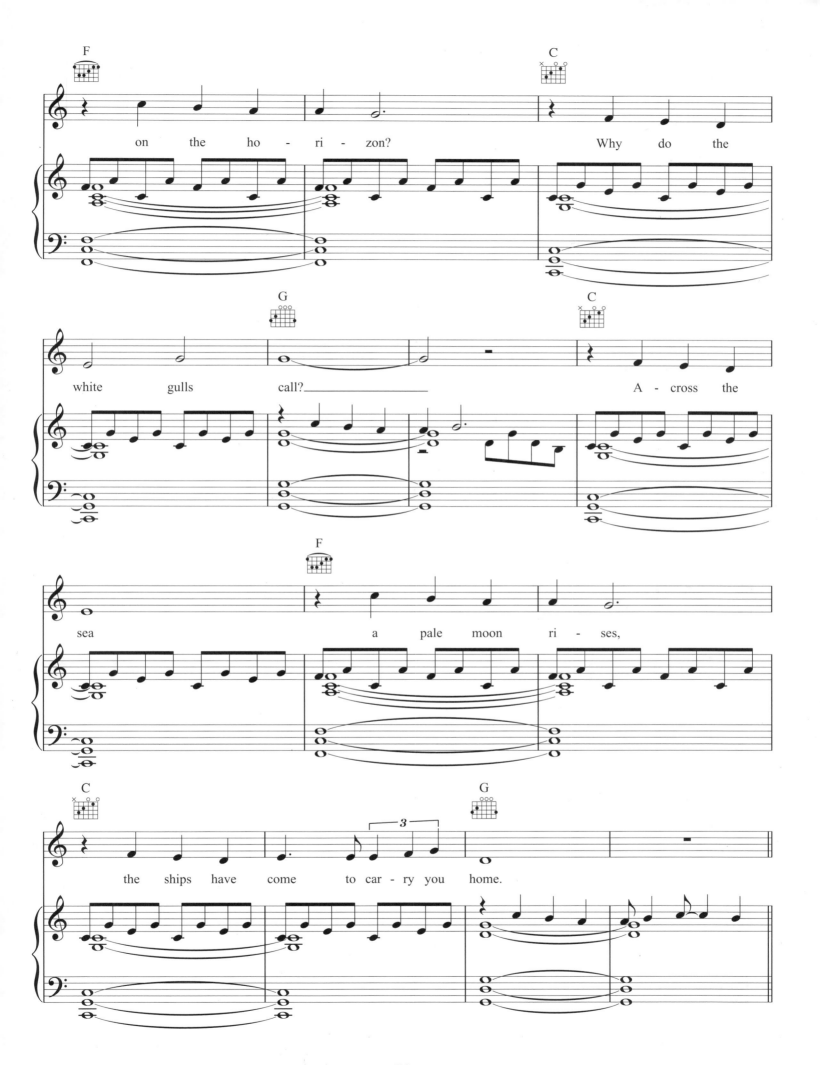

A KISS AT THE END OF THE RAINBOW

Words & Music by Michael McKean & Annette O'Toole

82

LA VIE EN ROSE

Words by Edith Piaf
Music by R.S. Louiguy

MAD WORLD

Words & Music by Roland Orzabal

Cello 2° only till *

1. All a-round me are fa-mil-iar fa-ces, worn out pla-ces,
2. Chil-dren wait-ing for the day they feel good, hap-py birth-day,

worn out fa-ces. Bright and ear-ly for their dai-ly ra-ces,
hap-py birth-day. And I feel the way that ev-'ry child should

MAN OF THE HOUR

Words & Music by Eddie Vedder

1. Ti - dal waves don't beg for - give - ness, crash, then on their way.
2. Na - ture has it's own re - li - gion, gos - pel from the land.

man of____ the hour____ has tak - en   his fi - nal   bow.____   As the____

___ cur - tain__comes down____   I__ feel   that this__ is   just____   good - bye   for

a tempo

now.

MONA LISA

Words & Music by Jay Livingston & Ray Evans

cold and lone-ly____ love-ly work of art?

art? Mo - na Li - sa.____

Mo - na Li - sa.____

PEOPLE AIN'T NO GOOD

Words & Music by Nick Cave

Peo - ple just   ain't no good,   I   think that's well

un-der-stood. You can see it ev-'ry-where you look,

peo-ple just ain't no good. We were mar-ried un-der

cher - ry trees,
- sons went.
hearts they're bad,

un-der blos-som we made our vows.
The wind has stripped the blos-soms bare,
they can com - fort you, some ev - en try.

All the blos-soms come sail-ing down,
A dif-f'rent tree now lines the streets,
They nurse you when you're ill of health.

through the streets and through the
shak-ing it's fists in the
They bu - ry you when you

107

PAPA LOVES MAMBO

Words & Music by Al Hoffman, Dick Manning & Bix Reichner

left,　　　　　　　she goes　right.____　　　　　　(Pa - pa's

look - ing for Ma - ma, but　Ma - ma is no - where in　sight.)

To Coda ⊕

(Uh!)　3. Pa - pa loves mam - bo,　　　　　　Ma -
　(4.) - pa loves mam - bo,　　　　　　Ma -

- ma loves mam - bo.　　　　　　Hav - ing their fling____ a - gain,
- ma loves mam - bo.　　　　　　Don't play the rum - ba and

A SONG FOR YOU

Words & Music by Gram Parsons & Chris Hillman

And to-mor-row we may still___ be___ there.___

THE SCARLET TIDE

Words & Music by Elvis Costello & T-Bone Burnett

2.Man goes be-yond his own de-ci-sion, gets caught up in a me-cha-ni-sm of swin-d-lers who act like___ kings, and bro-kers who break ev-'ry-thing. The dark of night was swift-ly fad-ing, close to the

dawn of day. why would I want___ him just to lose him a - gain.

We'll rise a - bove the scar - let tide that trick - les down through___ the

1.

moun - tain, and se - pa - rates the wi - dow from the bride. We'll rise a -

2.

bride.

poco rit.

A WALTZ FOR A NIGHT

Words & Music by Julie Delpy

123456789